COWBOYS
and the songs
they sang

COWBOYS & the songs they sang

by S. J. SACKETT, settings by LIONEL NOWAK, designed by WALTER EINSEL

published by WILLIAM R. SCOTT, INC., New York

LIBRARY OF CONGRESS CATALOG NO. 66-17571
TEXT (EXCLUSIVE OF FOLKSONGS) © 1967 by SAMUEL J. SACKETT
MUSICAL ACCOMPANIMENTS © 1967 by LIONEL NOWAK

ABOUT THE SONGS

The songs in this book all used to be sung by cowboys. Most date back to the twenty years (1870-1890) when the West was wildest and woolliest. The pictures come from around that time, too, so that you can see what things looked like.

Some of these songs were sort of lullabies sung to cattle at night to reassure them that cowboys were around to take care of them; some were sung on the move (these have the rolling rhythm of riding). All of them were sung around campfires as well.

Cowboys sang a great many more songs than any book could hold. The ones we print here are all about cowboy life, but cowboys sang many songs that weren't—ballads like *Barbara Allen*, and other English, Scottish, or Irish songs—even sailing songs. They often took tunes from these older songs to go with verses they made up about themselves and their own way of life.

Some songs in this book have a great many verses that go on and on. We have chosen the verses that tell most about cowboy life. There are also different versions. Our words for *The Streets of Laredo*, for instance, may not be the same as words you may know, and there are at least two completely different tunes (one from Ireland long before the town of Laredo existed). There are even different titles for this song—*The Cowboy's Lament*, *Once in the Saddle*, *The Dying Cowboy*, and *Tom Sherman's Barroom*—as well as *The Streets of Laredo*.

You can see from this that there is no "correct" version of these songs—no single composer to be true to. This is folk music, apt to change a little with each singer who sings. If you want to sing these songs differently or make up new verses of your own, go ahead. Everybody else has. By now they belong to you as much as to anyone else; that is what makes them folk music.

ABOUT THE PHOTOGRAPHS

To two active cowboys who were photographers, we owe most of the photographs in this book. Erwin Smith worked on most of the major Texas ranches at the turn of this century. About the time he came east to study art in 1907, Charles J. Belden was beginning to record cowboy life further north in Wyoming. Mr. Belden's photographs are reproduced with his permission. Erwin Smith's marvelous legacy of pictures is now in the Library of Congress and is reproduced with their help and with the permission of his sister, Mrs. L. C. Pettis.

CONTENTS

On The Trail

ON THE TRAIL

In the twenty-five years or so after the Civil War, the Eastern states of the U. S. became so crowded with people that there was no longer room for big cattle ranches. Cattle have to be raised where there is plenty of land to graze on—as much as sixteen acres to feed each animal in a herd. If you had a few thousand steers to feed, you would need a lot of land, and the West was where the land was.

On the other hand, the East was where most of the people lived, so that when the cattle were sent where they were needed most for food, they had to go East. That is still a long, long way, particularly if you have to walk most of it, and at first there were no railroads from the Western ranch country to the Eastern cities. So cowboys had to drive herds over long distances on what were called "trail drives" or "cattle drives."

Sometimes these drives would go all the way from a ranch in Texas to one of the big cities like Chicago which served as markets. This had its problems. The more walking an animal did, the more weight he lost. And since the owner was paid by the pound, the longer the animals walked, the less money he got for his beef.

Railroads came to be the answer to this problem, when after the Civil War, they began to be built across the United States. Now, on part of the journey at least, the cattle could ride in cattle cars without loss of weight.

The songs in this section are all about what life was like on the trail when, day after day, cowboys had to keep their herd moving, and when, night after night, some of them had to ride round and round the resting cattle to keep them from straying or getting excited.

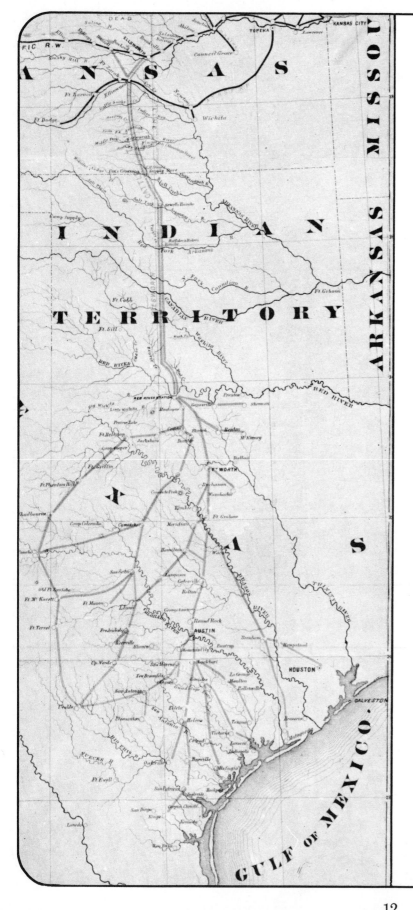

THE OLD CHISHOLM TRAIL

Joseph G. McCoy, a Texas cattleman, started it all in 1867. He established a cattle-shipping center at Abilene, Kansas, which at that time was about as far west as the Union Pacific railroad had been built. Then his cowboys began driving his cattle north from his ranch in Texas over the Chisholm trail to Abilene.

The Chisholm trail had come to be, so the story goes, because the year before, an Indian trader named Jesse Chisholm had driven a heavily loaded wagon north from San Antonio, Texas, to Wichita, Kansas, where his trading post was located. The wheels of the heavy wagon had made deep ruts, and McCoy's cowboys followed these wagon tracks to Wichita, striking out due north for Abilene from there.

In the next few years, hundreds of Texas herds—thousands upon thousands of cattle—were driven north through Oklahoma into Kansas. At first they went to Abilene, then to Ellsworth and Hays City as the Union Pacific was built westward, and then to Wichita and Dodge City as the Santa Fe was built. These towns would take care of the herds that would converge there to wait their turn for shipment.

Later, the land over which the cattle passed was fenced for farming, which made these trips impossible. Luckily, though, the establishment of railroad lines into Texas also made the long drives unnecessary, and the trail-driving days were done.

This song about the trail is full of the cowboy's complaints about his job—the weather, the long hours, the bad food—and his insistence that he wants to quit punching cows.

You may not know all the cowboy words used in this song. The cowboy who sings this version of the song is trail driving the **Lone Star herd**—a herd of cattle from the Lone Star ranch and marked with the Lone Star brand. Probably there never was a Lone Star herd, but since Texas is called the Lone Star state, the cowboy is pretending that there is a Lone Star herd which stands for all Texas cattle herds. The **horn** of the saddle is also sometimes called the pommel; it is the part that sticks up in the front of the saddle, and the cowboys used it to hang their ropes on. The **stirrup** is the footrest that hangs down on either side of the saddle. **Chaps** are leather leg coverings that the cowboys wear over their pants; they are called chaps because they protect the cowboys from getting their legs scratched when they ride through the chaparral (chop-a-RAHL in Spanish or shap-a-RAL in English), as the Spanish called the scrubby plants growing on Western hillsides. A **slicker** is a kind of raincoat. **Prairie hay** is just this cowboy's joking name for the buffalo grass that grows on the prairie. **Longhorn** cattle are one of the three kinds of cattle which were commonly raised in Texas—longhorn, shorthorn, and Brahma. In the 1860's and 1870's, most Texas cattle were longhorns. "Oh, my seat's in the saddle, and my saddle's in the sky, and I'll quit punching cows in the sweet by-and-by" (an expression from an old hymn meaning the hereafter), tells you that, despite all he has to complain about, he is not really going to quit his work in this life, and even when his "saddle is in the sky" he still sees himself as sitting in it.

THE OLD CHISHOLM TRAIL

Well, come a - long, boys, and lis - ten to my tale; I'll

tell you of my trou - bles on the old Chis - holm Trail. Come a - ti - yi yip - py, yip - py

yay, yip - py yay, Come a - ti - yi yip - py yip - py yay.

With a ten-dollar horse and a forty-dollar saddle,
I started in herding these Texas cattle. (*Chorus*)

I started up the trail October twenty-third;
I started up the trail with the Lone Star herd. (*Chorus*)

I jumped in the saddle and grabbed hold of the horn,
The best cowpuncher that ever was born. (*Chorus*)

My foot in the stirrup, my seat in the saddle,
The best cowpuncher that ever rode a-straddle. (*Chorus*)

I'm on my horse, and I'm going on the run,
The quickest-shooting cowboy that ever pulled a gun. (*Chorus*)

No chaps, no slicker, and it's pouring down rain,
I vow I'll never night-herd again. (*Chorus*)

Out one night, it was pouring down hail,
I reached for my rope, got a calf by the tail. (*Chorus*)

I'm up in the morning before daylight;
Before I sleep the moon shines bright. (*Chorus*)

Oh, it's bacon and beans most every day,
I'd as soon be eating this prairie hay. (*Chorus*)

We rounded 'em up and put 'em in the cars,
And that was the end of the old Lone Stars. (*Chorus*)

I'm going to sell my horse, going to sell my saddle,
'Cause I'm tired of punching these longhorn cattle. (*Chorus*)

Farewell to the trail, I wish you no harm;
I'm going to quit herding to go on the farm. (*Chorus*)

Oh, my seat's in the saddle, and my saddle's in the sky,
And I'll quit punching cows in the sweet by-and-by. (*Chorus*)

GET ALONG, LITTLE DOGIES

Nobody now knows where the term **dogies** comes from, but it was first used by cowboys to describe calves whose mothers had died or who had become separated from them. Later it was used for any calf as the cowboys' affectionate term for the animals they herded.

This song, which is sung at a fast tempo which matches the rhythm of the horse's gait on a trail drive, shows by the places named that it originated later than some of the other songs in this book, for it dates from the time when Wyoming, Montana, and Idaho began to be centers of the cattle industry in the 1880's. The cattle are being driven from Texas, where they were born, to summer grazing grounds in Wyoming—grounds which the cowboy who sings the song apparently does not think much of, for he says that the dogies will find nothing there but **prickly pear** and **cholla** (pronounced CHOY-a), which are two kinds of cactus. Then, when they are fattened up, the dogies will be taken to Idaho and sold to the government as food for the Indians on reservations there.

When the Indians were free, they used to hunt and eat buffalo. But when the government put them on reservations, they could not do this any longer, and the government had to provide food for them. The cowboy knows that these dogies are going to end up in some Indian squaw's beef stew.

Chuck was the cowboys' word for food, and when the trail drive was going on, the cook went along driving a **chuck wagon.** At mealtime he would stop and fix the cowboys' food; they would ride in from wherever they were and eat. It was hard work to keep the cattle moving. They wanted to stop and eat grass where they were, but the cowboys had to keep making them **roll on.**

16

GET ALONG, LITTLE DOGIES

As I was out walk-ing one morn-ing for plea-sure, I saw a cow punch-er come rid-ing a - long; His hat was thrown back and his spurs were all jing-ling, And as he ap-proached he was sing-ing this song: Whoo-pee ti yi yo, get a - long, lit-tle do-gies! It's your mis-for-tune and none of my own. Whoo-pee ti yi yo, get a-long lit-tle do-gies, For you know Wy-o-ming will be your new home!

Early in the spring we round up the dogies,
Mark 'em and brand 'em and bob off their tails,
Round up our horses, and load the chuck wagon,
Then throw the dogies out on the trail. (*Chorus*)

It's whooping and yelling and driving the dogies—
Oh, how I wish that they'd go on!—
It's whooping and punching and go on little dogies,
For you know Wyoming will be your new home. (*Chorus*)

When the night comes on, we herd them on the bedground,
These little dogies that roll on so slow;
Roll up the herd and cut out the strays,
And roll the little dogies that never rolled before. (*Chorus*)

You lived with your mothers way down in Texas,
Where the jimson weed and sand burrs grow;
Now all you'll find is prickly pear and cholla,
Till you are ready for the trail to Idaho. (*Chorus*)

Oh, you'll be soup for Uncle Sam's Indians,
It's "Beef, heap beef" I hear them cry;
Get along, get along, get along, little dogies,
You're going to be beef steers by and by. (*Chorus*)

THE NIGHT-HERDING SONG

On the trail, a herd of cattle could at any time become a screaming, bellowing juggernaut that could kill men who got in its way, destroy equipment, run off precious pounds of weight, and get scattered and lost. The cowboys had a word for this—**stampede!**

Stampedes were especially dangerous and especially likely to occur at night. In the quiet prairie night, the slightest noise, even the sudden crackling of a twig if a sleeping cow rolled on it, could send the herd alert and charging over the plains. And in the short-grass country, thunderstorms could come up suddenly. A dull rolling boom in the distance or a sharp crack of lightning nearby was a real danger to cowboys trying to keep the herd together.

But the sound of a human voice quieted the cattle. It reassured them that everything was all right, that somebody was there who would take care of them and protect them from harm. So cowboys "riding the night herd"—circling around the sleeping animals—took to singing lullabies as they rode. These were called "night-herding songs," and the one printed here is the best known.

Night-herding songs served two other important purposes. First, they let any **rustlers** (cattle thieves) who might be in the neighborhood know that the cowboys were on guard. Second, they helped keep the cowboys themselves awake. On the trail, the cowboys had to ride with the herd all day and then go wearily out again at night when the herd camped. Not all of them were needed to ride every night. The trail boss would have them take turns so that each cowboy would get to sleep every other night, or perhaps two nights out of three. Even so, it was hard to keep awake riding the night herd after having ridden hard all day, and singing helped.

THE NIGHT-HERDING SONG

Oh, slow up, do-gies, quit roam-ing a - round; You have wan-dered and tram-pled all o-ver the ground. Oh, graze a-long, do-gies, and move kind of slow, And don't be al-ways on the go. Move slow, lit-tle do-gies, move slow. — Hi - yo, hi - yo, — hi - yo. —

Oh, say, little dogies, when will you lie down
And give up this shifting and roving around?
My horse is leg-weary, and I'm awfully tired,
But if you get away I am sure to be fired.
Lie down, little dogies, lie down.
Hi-yo, hi-yo, hi-yo.

Oh, lie still, dogies, since you have lain down;
Stretch away out on the big open ground.
Snore loud, little dogies, and drown the wild sound;
It'll go away when the day rolls around.
Lie still, little dogies, lie still.
Hi-yo, hi-yo, hi-yo.

THE RAILROAD CORRAL

At every cowtown there was a **corral,** or pen for the cattle, built along the tracks. Even today, as you ride a train through the West, you can see railroad corrals along the tracks. When the cowboys got their cattle into these railroad corrals, their job was almost over. All they had left to do then was make the cattle get into the cattle cars, but that was always a hard job because the animals didn't want to get in. Often the cowboys had to punch them with long poles to make them move. That is the reason cowboys are sometimes called **cowpunchers.**

This song describes the cowboy's life on the trail as he travels toward his goal of the railroad corral. He is up before dawn and eats a breakfast of **flapjacks** (or pancakes) while the night riders who have been guarding the herd rouse the cattle and get them started on the trail. Then he saddles his horse and tightens the **cinch,** the belt around the horse that keeps the saddle on. He mounts and takes hold of the **reins,** the leather straps attached to a metal bar between the horse's teeth called a **bit,** by which the rider controls the horse. Then he goes looking in the brush to see whether any of the **steers,** or cattle, have strayed into it during the night.

As the drive goes on, the day gets hotter and hotter. A herd of cattle raises a lot of dust, and the heat and dust make the cowboy thirsty. (The cowboys last to be hired were always put at the rear of the herd, which was the dustiest and most unpleasant position. After they had worked long enough to prove that they were good at their job, they were promoted to the sides of the herd, and newer cowboys took their place in the back.) The cowboy knows that the **trail boss,** who is in charge of the drive, has planned to reach a river or creek by noon so that cattle and men can have a drink. The thought of the cool, refreshing water makes the cowboy feel better, as also does the thought that every mile they travel brings them that much nearer to the railroad corral, nearer to the end of the gruelling trail drive, nearer to a town with all sorts of facilities for whoopee.

The Railroad Corral is also sometimes sung to the tune of *The Irish Washerwoman,* which was very popular at frontier square dances. The tune used for it here is a common one for cowboy songs; many sets of words have been sung to it.

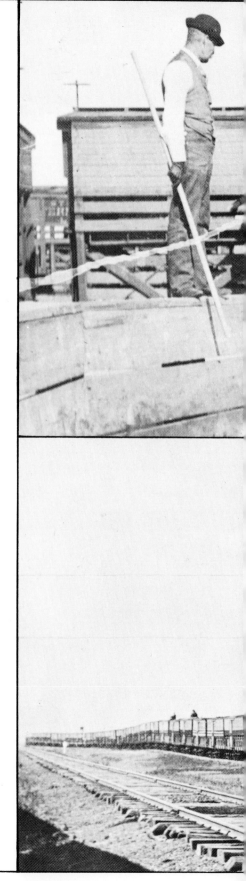

THE RAILROAD CORRAL

Oh, we're up in the morn - ing be - fore break of day, The —

chuck wag - on's bus - y, the flap - jack's in play; The

herd is a - stir o - ver hill - side and glen, With the

night rid - ers start - ing them down trail a - gain.

So come tighten your cinches and shake out your reins,
Wake up your old bronco and make for the plains;
Come roust out your steers from the thick chapparal,
For the outfit is off for the railroad corral.

As the sun circles upward, the steers as they plod
Are pounding to powder the hot prairie sod;
It seems when the dust makes you dizzy and sick
That we'll never reach noon and the cool, shady crick.

But tie up your kerchief, give spurs to your nag,
Come dry up your grumbles and try not to lag;
Keep punching those steers through the thick chapparal,
For we're well on our way to the railroad corral.

chapter II

On The Range

ON THE RANGE

The long trail drive took skill and endurance, but range life wasn't easy either. There were many things a cowboy had to know how to do well. He had to know how to ride a horse and how to tame a wild one so he could stay on its back. He had to know how to train his horses to help him in his job—a job that demanded coordination and understanding between horse and rider, and he needed to keep his horses healthy, so that they would serve him well.

Then he had to know how to rope a steer or a calf, how to throw it to the ground, and how to brand it by burning the symbol of his ranch on its hip. He had to know how to take care of the cattle so they would grow and bring a high price when they were ready for market.

The cowboy's job had to be done when it was raining, when it was blazing hot, whether it was day or night, no matter if he was tired or sick. His job was dangerous. He might be trampled by the cattle, thrown from his horse, or shot by a rustler. And danger might come from poisonous rattlesnakes or from tornadoes or blizzards.

Because it was hard, dangerous, skilled work, the cowboy was proud of what he could do—so proud that he might boast he could rope and tie a calf for branding faster than anyone within earshot, or that he could stay on a bucking horse longer. This would lead to contests. Out of such contests grew **rodeos** (at first pronounced as in Spanish—ro-DAY-o—but now the people who compete and who watch usually pronounce the word ROAD-ee-o). When the nature of the cowboy's work began to change, it was performing in rodeos that kept the old skills alive.

In our day many things have combined to make the work of the cowboy far different from the life that is described and shown in these songs and pictures. Refrigeration means that meat, instead of live animals, can be shipped long distances, and there are so many railroads that the long trail drives are no longer necessary.

As new methods began to change the cowboy's job, the old timers were saddened. The ways they knew weren't used any more. The skills they knew weren't needed. The West they knew was gone. Only the rodeo was left.

29

THE STRAWBERRY ROAN

Instead of raising their horses carefully from colts, cowboys let them run wild until they were needed. These wild horses were called **mustangs** or **broncos.** Sometimes a wild horse was also called a **cayuse.**

When a cowboy needed a horse, he went out on the range and captured a mustang by roping it. Then came the problem of taming it, for a wild horse is a very independent animal and resents having a man on its back. Until tamed, or "broken," the horse would jump and buck and try to throw the man off its back. Taming the bronco was the job of the **bronco-buster,** an experienced cowboy who got on the wild horse and rode it until it finally gave up and got used to being ridden, so that less experienced riders could take over.

Today one of the chief attractions of a rodeo is the bronco-riding contest, in which cowboys see who can stay on a bucking bronco for the longest time. In fact, nowadays there are many cowboys who never herded cows, but who go all over the country performing in rodeos.

A **roan** horse is one with large splotches of a dark color on a white or a light gray background; a **strawberry** roan would be one on which this dark color was red. When the cowboy in the song says that he will **fan** the strawberry roan, he refers to the fact that the bronco-buster holds on with only one hand while he waves the other,

usually with his hat in it, to keep his balance. It looks as if he were fanning the horse with his hat. The **44 brand** means that the brand, or symbol, of the ranch that owns the horse is "44," and these numbers have been burned into the horse's hip to identify his ownership. If the horse's leg was **spavined,** he had a bony growth on the inside of his hock, or ankle, probably because he had sprained it and the sprain had not healed properly. If he had **pigeon toes,** his hooves pointed inward. If he had a crick in his neck, the muscles were stiff and he held it at an unusual angle. A **Roman nose** curves down like an eagle's beak. The cowboy's **twine** was his rope, his lariat or lasso. "First came the **hobbles**" means that the cowboys hobbled the horse, or tied its legs, so that it could not run. Then, after the bronco-buster got into the saddle, the cowboys untied it. When a cowboy **cinches** his saddle, he tightens it, in just the same way that you tighten your belt. When a horse began trying to throw off his rider, cowboys said that he was **unwinding. Sunfishing** is a special kind of bucking movement that some horses make, which looks like the movements of a quick-darting sunfish; a horse that sunfishes is especially difficult to ride. **Nome** is in Alaska. There aren't any cowboys there, but the singer of this song wanted a place that was a long way from Texas to show an especially big distance.

31

THE STRAWBERRY ROAN

I was hang-ing round town and just wast-ing my time, Out of a
job and not earn-ing a dime, When a fel-low stepped up and he
said, "I sup-pose You're a bronc-bust-ing man by the looks of your clothes." "I'm a
bronc-bust-ing man and a good one," I claimed, "Do you hap-pen to
have an-y bad ones to tame?" He said, "I've got one, a

straw - ber - ry roan, And the man who gets on him is sure to be thrown."

Well, he said that this pony was a good one to buck
And at throwing bronc riders he sure had the luck,
And I asked what he'd pay if I were to stay
Just to ride that old pony around for a day.
He offered ten dollars; I said, "I'm your man,
For the bronc wasn't living that I couldn't fan;
No, the bronc wasn't living and never drew breath
That I couldn't ride till he starved plumb to death."

(Chorus)

Well, bright in the morning and right after chuck,
I went to the corral to see that pony buck,
And down in the corner and standing alone
Was that pig-eyed old cayuse, the strawberry roan.
He had little pin ears that were split at the tip,
A big 44 brand across his left hip;
His legs were all spavined, and he had pigeon toes,
A crick in his neck and a big Roman nose.

(Chorus)

When I opened the gate, he threw up his head,
And he looked at me cross-eyed with eyes that were red;
So I put on my spurs and I shook out my twine,
And I told the old stranger ten dollars were mine.
First came the hobbles, and there was a fight
While I threw on my saddle and cinched it down tight;
Then I got up on top. I was feeling just fine
As I said, "Let him go, boys, and let him unwind."

(Chorus)

Say, that little old pony—say, he sure unwound;
He never spent much of his time on the ground;
He was just the worst bucker I've seen on the range;
He could turn on a nickel and give you some change.
I went up with a jerk and came down with a bump;
I tell you that strawberry cayuse could jump!
He bucked high in the east and sunfished in the west;
Just stay on his middle—that was my best.

(Chorus)

I lost both my stirrups and also my hat;
I held on with both hands, though as blind as a bat.
With a big forward lunge he went up on high,
Left me sitting on nothing way up in the sky;
I turned over twice, and I came back to earth,
And I hit the ground blaming the day of his birth.
Now I know there are ponies that I cannot ride;
Some are still living, they haven't all died.

(Final Chorus)

Chorus

Well, it's Oh, that straw-ber-ry roan! Oh, that straw-ber-ry

roan! He goes up in the east and comes down in the west; Just to

stay in the sad-dle I'm do-ing my best. Stay on that straw-ber-ry

roan! Stay on that straw-ber-ry roan!

Final Chorus: Well, it's Oh, that strawberry roan!
Oh, that strawberry roan!
That sunfishing bronco is well left alone;
There isn't a cowboy from Texas to Nome
Who could ride that strawberry roan.
Stay off that strawberry roan!

THE ZEBRA DUN

The cowboy's life was rough, and the jokes he liked to play on people were often rough, too, particularly on newcomers to the West, who seldom knew, and often didn't care about, the skills cowboys respected. Such a newcomer they called a **tenderfoot** (a cowboy's feet grew tough from rubbing against his boots all day) or a **greenhorn,** after the young cattle whose horns begin growing when spring plants begin to grow green. So the cowboys in this song are going to play a trick on the "greenhorn" who was "just escaped from town."

The Cimarron River has its **head**—that is, starts—in northeastern New Mexico, not far from where the Santa Fe railroad enters New Mexico through Raton Pass (usually ruh-TONN.) The stranger must have been working for the railroad, perhaps at the town of Raton, which is only about eighty-five miles west of the Oklahoma border. After he left his job, he was going east toward Oklahoma, looking for work on a ranch there; the **Seven D** must have been the name of the ranch.

A **dun** horse is a dull grayish-brown color. Why this one is called a **zebra** dun isn't clear. Perhaps the horse had stripes that reminded the cowboys of those on a zebra. Or there may have been a ranch called the Z Bar that the horse had originally belonged to, and when the song was first made the horse was the Z Bar dun; then, when people began to sing the song who didn't know about the Z Bar ranch, they may have used "zebra" because "Z Bar" didn't mean anything to them.

THE ZEBRA DUN

We were camped on the plains at the head of the Cim - ar - on, When a
long came a stran - ger who stopped to ar - gue some. He
looked so ver - y fool - ish, we be - gan to look a - round; we
thought he was a green - horn just es - caped from town.

Such an educated fellow, his thoughts just came in herds;
He astonished all those cowboys with his jaw-breaking words.
He just kept on talking till he made the boys all sick
And they began to think to see how they could play a trick.

He said he'd lost his job out on the Santa Fe,
Was bound across the plains now to strike the Seven D.
We asked him how it happened; he said, "Trouble with the boss,"
And asked if he could borrow a fat saddle horse.

This tickled all the boys to death, they laughed up their sleeves:
"We will lend you a fine horse, fresh and fat as you please."
Shorty grabbed a lariat and roped the Zebra Dun
And gave him to the stranger while we waited for the fun.

Old Dunny was an outlaw that had grown so awfully wild
That he could paw the moon down, he could jump for a mile;
But Dunny stood there still, just as if he didn't know,
Until we had him saddled and all readied to go.

When the stranger hit the saddle, old Dunny quit the earth
And traveled right straight upward for all that he was worth,
Pitching, squealing, screaming, and throwing wall-eyed fits,
His hind feet perpendicular, his front feet in the bits.

We could see the tops of mountains under Dunny's every jump,
But the stranger seemed to grow there, just like a camel's hump;
The stranger sat upon him and curled his black moustache
Like a summer boarder waiting for the hash.

He thumped him on the shoulders, and he spurred him when he whirled;
He showed all those cowpunchers who was top man in this world;
And when he had dismounted and stood there on the ground,
We knew he was a cowboy and not a gent from town.

The boss was standing close by, watching all the show;
He walked up to the stranger and said he needn't go:
"If you can use a lasso like you rode the Zebra Dun,
You're the man I've been looking for since the year One."

He spent the season with us, and the cowboys all agreed
There was nothing that he couldn't do, save stopping a stampede.
So there's one thing and a sure thing I've learned since I have been born,
Every educated fellow's not a plumb greenhorn.

I RIDE AN OLD PAINT

The easy, soothing tune of this song is well adapted to night-herding work. It contains so many cowboy expressions that perhaps the best way to explain them is to tell the same story in more familiar words.

"I ride a horse that is white with big splotches of black or brown that make the horse look as if paint had been splashed on him, and following me at the end of a rope is an old mother horse who carries my bedroll, cooking equipment, food, and other supplies. I'm going to Montana to bulldog steers, to grab their horns and wrestle them to the ground in rodeos. (This detail dates the song as after 1900, by the way, because bulldogging steers did not become a rodeo attraction until that date.) These horses I am riding graze in ravines and drink water from creeks. They have been on the trail for a long time, and their tails are matted with mud. Their backs are sore—the paint's because I have been riding on him for so long, the dam's because she has been carrying a heavy pack.

"Get along, little dogies, get along there slow, for my fiery paint (sometimes called a pinto) and my snuff-colored dam are rearing up, ready to go on." (Snuff is a kind of light reddish-brown color.)

The rest of the song is easy to understand without any explanation.

I RIDE AN OLD PAINT

I ride an old paint, and I lead an old dam, I'm going to Mon - ta - na to throw the hou - li - han. They feed in the cou - lees and wa - ter in the draw; Their tails are all mat - ted, and their backs are all raw. Get a - long, lit - tle do - gies, get a - long there slow, For the fier - y and the snuf - fy are rear - ing to go.

Oh, when I die, take my saddle from the wall,
Put it on my pony, lead him from his stall,
Tie my bones to his back, and turn our faces to the west;
We'll ride the prairies that we love the best. (*Chorus*)

chapter III

The Cowboy's Sorrows

THE COWBOY'S SORROWS
(And How He Drowned Them)

Though "riding the prairies we love best" was a pleasure, and though there was fun and excitement in the skills of the cowboy's job, there was boredom and loneliness as well. Often the range where he worked was a long way from town. Even when it wasn't, his job kept him too busy to get there much, and while he was on the trail, there was no chance at all. So cowboys rarely saw anybody except other cowboys. And, as often happens when men are together for a long time, they get sick of the sight of each other. They long to see a pretty girl or two, or just to go to town for the change and excitement and a hand of poker or faro.

In the 1860's and 1870's, a great many cowboys were men who had fought on one side or the other in the Civil War. They were restless and looking for excitement, and the West was said to be full of it. Some might have run away from home because of troubles with parents or the police. Southerners, particularly, often found their home towns changed by the war and without interesting jobs for them. A good many Negroes, former slaves who had just recently been freed by the Civil War, also found it hard to get work in the East. In fact there were probably more Negro than Northern cowboys. Many Negroes won success and esteem in a life where character was more important than color.

Many of these men who drifted west left parents, brothers, sisters, and best girls back East. And once they got onto some far-off ranch, they were apt to get homesick for the family and friends in the towns they had left behind.

I'M A POOR LONESOME COWBOY

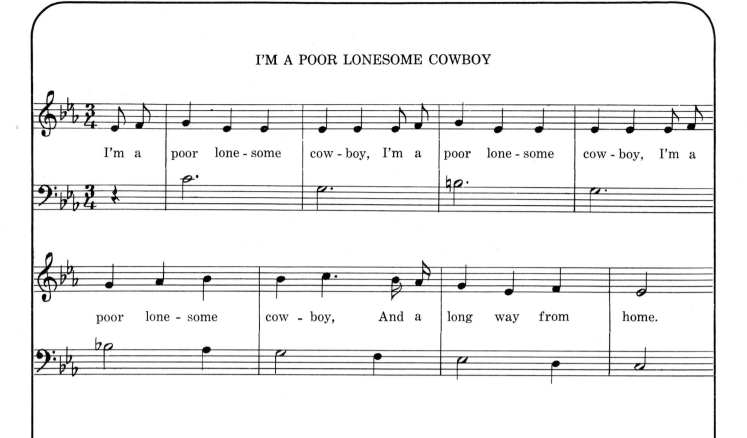

I'm a poor lone-some cow-boy, I'm a poor lone-some cow-boy, I'm a poor lone-some cow-boy, And a long way from home.

I don't have a father,
I don't have a father,
I don't have a father
To buy the clothes I wear.

I don't have a mother,
I don't have a mother,
I don't have a mother
To mend the clothes I wear.

I don't have a sister,
I don't have a sister,
I don't have a sister
To take good care of me.

I don't have a brother,
I don't have a brother,
I don't have a brother
To ride the range with me.

I don't have a father,
I don't have a mother,
No sister and no brother
To ride along with me.

I don't have a sweetheart,
I don't have a sweetheart,
I don't have a sweetheart
To sit and talk with me.

I'm a poor lonesome cowboy,
I'm a poor lonesome cowboy,
I'm a poor lonesome cowboy,
And a long way from home.

THE DYING COWBOY

"Oh, bur - y me not on the lone prai - rie" These words came low and mourn-ful - ly From the pal - lid lips

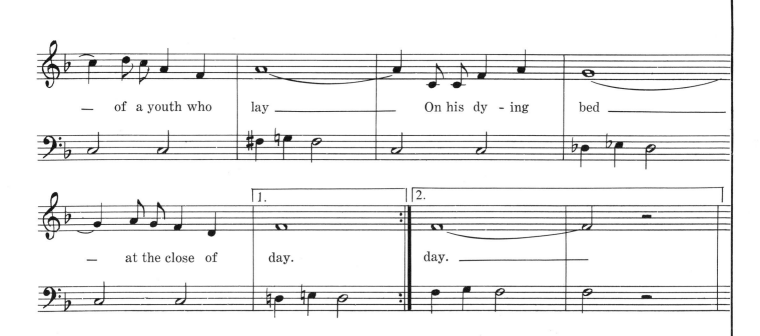

— of a youth who lay _____ On his dy - ing bed _____

— at the close of day. | 1. day. | 2. day. _____

"Oh, bury me not on the lone prairie
Where the coyotes howl and the wind blows free;
In a cold, cold grave don't bury me,
Oh, bury me not on the lone prairie.

"I wish to be laid where my mother's tears
And my sister's too can mingle there,
Where friends can come and weep o'er me;
Then bury me not on the lone prairie.

"It matters not, so I've been told,
Where the body lies when the heart grows cold.
But grant, oh! grant this boon to me
And bury me not on the lone prairie.

"Oh, bury me not—" and his voice failed there,
But we took no heed of his dying prayer;
In a narrow grave, just six by three,
We buried him there on the lone prairie.

TYING KNOTS IN THE DEVIL'S TAIL

Cowtowns had corrals for cows, and they had cardhouses, dancehalls, and saloons for cowboys. Of course, not all cowboys used them—many were sober, steady, quiet men. But others, with all their responsibilities loaded onto cattle cars, and a few weeks' wages in their pockets, were ready for violent celebration of their temporary freedom, with plenty of liquor to wash away problems and loneliness.

The cowtown was no substitute for home, but it was a relief from the dry, dreary, dusty trail. The cowboy often tried to pack all the excitement he had been missing into a few days there —drinking, dancing, gambling, brawling with other cowboys. After being away from people for so long, he had forgotten how to act around them. He might even "tree the town"—riding at full gallop down the main street with pistols blazing, breaking store windows, and sending sober citizens scurrying for cover.

Of course, when it was all over, there were still the same problems, and usually a headache as well. But apparently many cowboys thought that those few hours of feeling as if they didn't have a care in the world were worth the price they had to pay for them.

Anyway, the cowboys in this uproarious song evidently rode into town to get drunk. That achieved, they rode back, met the Devil, fought him, and won—in the song, at least.

Any Westerner would know that Sagebrush Sam and Rusty Jiggs were rustlers, because they used a running iron rather than a regular branding iron, or stamp iron. A stamp iron burns a design in the hide of the calf. It always makes the same design. A running iron is made so that you can draw with it, like a pencil. Rustlers use running irons because they can change the brand that is already on the calf. Sagebrush Sam and Rusty Jiggs were taking any stray calf that came near—and changing its brand to theirs. They were also putting a mark in the calves' ears by cutting out a little notch, so that when cowboys from the ranches in the neighborhood came by looking for strays, Sam and Rusty could claim them all as having their own markings, both brand and notch. They had better hide their running iron, though. In some states it is a crime just to own one.

The two rustlers were working in the Sierra Nevada Mountains. Sagebrush Sam calls what they were doing "cowography." There really isn't any such word, but if there were, it would mean "writing on cows."

After forty drinks, they wouldn't know what actually happened on the way back to their camp. Certainly they couldn't really have met the Devil and tied him up. What do you think happened? Do you think perhaps they met a steer and were so drunk they thought he was the Devil? Or do you think perhaps the whole thing happened only in their imaginations?

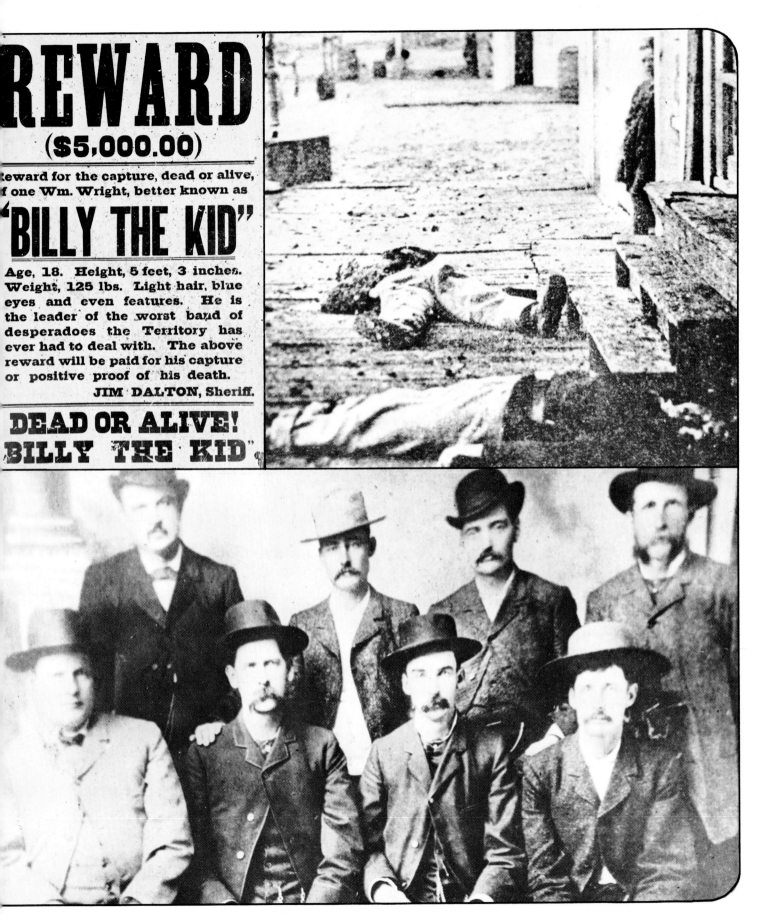

REWARD
($5,000.00)

Reward for the capture, dead or alive, of one Wm. Wright, better known as

"BILLY THE KID"

Age, 18. Height, 5 feet, 3 inches. Weight, 125 lbs. Light hair, blue eyes and even features. He is the leader of the worst band of desperadoes the Territory has ever had to deal with. The above reward will be paid for his capture or positive proof of his death.

JIM DALTON, Sheriff.

DEAD OR ALIVE!
BILLY THE KID

TYING KNOTS IN THE DEVIL'S TAIL

Way up yon-der in the Sier-ra peaks, Where the yel-low jack pines grow tall,

Sage-brush Sam and Rus-ty Jiggs had a round-up camp last fall.

They took their ponies and their running irons
And maybe a dog or two,
And they vowed they'd brand every long-eared calf
That came within their view.

Well, many a flop-eared dogie
That wandered along that day
Got his long ears whittled and his old hide scorched
In a most artistic way.

Says Sagebrush Sam to Rusty Jiggs,
As he throws his running iron down,
"I'm getting tired of cowography,
And I reckon I'll go to town."

So they saddled their ponies and struck a lope,
For it was a long old ride;
But those were the days when an old cowpoke
Could oil up his old insides.

Well, they started out at the Kentucky Bar
At the head of Whisky Row,
And they ended up at the Depot House
Just forty drinks below.

Well, as they were coming back to camp,
Packing that awful load,
Who should they meet but the Devil himself,
Come prancing down the road.

Now, the Devil said, "You ornery skunks,
You'd better go hunt your holes,
For I've come up from the rim-rocks of Hell
To gather in your souls."

Said Rusty Jiggs, "We're just from town
And feeling kind of tight;
You're not going to get any cowboy souls
Without some kind of a fight."

So he punched a hole in his old throw-rope
And he threw it straight and true,
And he roped the Devil around both horns,
And he had it anchored true.

Now, Sagebrush Sam was a lariat man
With his rope all coiled up neat,
So he shook it out and he built him a loop,
And he roped the Devil's hind feet.

They threw him down on the desert ground
While they got their irons red hot,
And they put a crop in the devil's ears,
And they branded him a lot.

And then they sawed off the Devil's horns
And knotted his tail for a joke;
Then they left him there in the Sierra peaks,
Tied up to a black-jack oak.

Well, if you've ever traveling the Sierra peaks
And you hear a terrible wail,
You'll know it's nothing but the Devil himself
And he's crying 'bout the knots in his tail.

THE STREETS OF LAREDO

Not all cowboy sprees ended as comically as that of Sagebrush Sam and Rusty Jiggs. This song, one of the saddest and mournfulest of all cowboy songs—also one of the most beautiful—tells a far different kind of story.

Laredo is a town in southern Texas, just across the Rio Grande from Mexico. It would be unusual to see a cowboy in a suit of **white linen,** though not impossible, for such a suit would be cool in the hot Texas weather; more likely the "white linen" of the song refers to a sheet in which the cowboy's body would be wrapped for burial. Indeed, some versions of the song have the words "wrapped in white linen." The **death march** would be a march (but played slowly) to which the funeral procession would go from the church, where services were held, to the graveyard where the cowboys were buried. **Boot Hill** was a common name for a frontier cemetery, because so many of the people buried there "died with their boots on." **Rosie's** probably was a frontier dancehall. The reference to the **card house** implies that the cowboy was shot in an argument over a game of cards. Most cowboys loved to play cards, and many gamblers who played with them would try to beat them by cheating. Many times shooting started when a cowboy caught a gambler cheating at cards, or when someone was wrongly accused of cheating.

You will notice, in the next to last verse, that the last line is cut short—abrupt as death. The last verse is the same as the second except the word "me" changes to "him." The young cowboy's last instruction is repeated for him since he can no longer speak for himself.

THE STREETS OF LAREDO

"Oh, play the fife slowly and beat the drum lowly,
And play the death march as you bear me along;
Just take me to Boot Hill and chuck the sod o'er me,
For I'm a young cowboy and I know I've done wrong.

"I see by your outfit that you are a cowboy,"
These words he spoke as he saw me ride by;
"Come sit here beside me and hear my sad story,
For I'm shot through the body and know I must die.

"Oh, once in the saddle I used to go dashing,
Oh, once in the saddle I used to ride high;
But I went to Rosie's and then to the card house,
Got shot through the body, and now here I lie.

"Oh, bring me a glass of cold water, cold water,
Just bring me a glass of cold water," he said;
But when I returned with the glass of cold water,
The poor young cowboy was dead.

Oh, play the fife slowly and beat the drum lowly,
And play the death march as you bear him along;
Just take him to Boot Hill and chuck the sod o'er him,
For he's a young cowboy and he knows he's done wrong.

chapter IV

The

Cowboy's Love & Dreams

THE COWBOY'S LOVES AND DREAMS

When the cowboy was feeling at his loneliest and most miserable, what did he dream of? Perhaps to meet a nice girl, marry her, and have a home and children. But out on the range where he was for months at a time, there were generally no girls at all, and on the few occasions when he got to town it was hard to meet the nice ones. He had plenty of chances to meet dance-hall hostesses and other women of that type, but they were interested less in him than in getting some of the money he had just collected for his long weeks of work. And if somehow he did meet someone nice, he had little opportunity on his infrequent visits to court her before some townsman married her.

If the cowboy really felt like marrying some nice girl, why didn't he quit his job, go to town, and find steady work? The answer must be that really, underneath it all, he didn't want to. The cowboy usually looked down on the townsman. This was partly because he was uneasy in town, and made up for this by pretending he was better than the people who lived there.

There were, of course, a few cowboys who did settle down and go to work in town. Others homesteaded—that is, settled on land owned by the government, built a house on it, and were then given the land in return for putting it to use. A few saved their money and were able to buy ranches of their own.

Most cowboys, though, just stayed cowboys until their active days were done. Then it was too late to learn anything else, so they stayed on around the ranch houses, doing odd jobs, helping out by cooking or feeding the animals.

Perhaps dread of this kind of uselessness, as well as the hardship, danger, and loneliness of the cowboy life he was living, led many a young man to think he would quit it. But while he was still good at bulldogging a steer or riding a bronc, why should he change—just yet? Why begin all over in a new job he might not even be good at and in a citified way of life all strange and different from the outdoor solitude he had come to love?

So the cowboy longed for a girl he could love and marry. But often, if he ever did find her, he also found himself not quite ready to give up his free way of life for her.

THE TWO TRAILS

Although both these songs tell of cowboys leaving the girls they loved, they couldn't be less alike. The one is spare, the other is windy and self-pitying.

In *The Trail to Mexico* the singer tells, with dates and details, how badly he had been treated, how none of it was his fault, and how he will never trust women again.

The Colorado Trail is only four lines long. These few words tell no sure story of what happened, but in them is packed all the despair of turning away from love and companionship to head down the trail of life alone.

THE COLORADO TRAIL

Eyes like the morn-ing star, | Cheek like a rose, | Lau-ra was a pret-ty girl,

Hea - ven on - ly knows. Weep, all ye lit - tle rains, Wail, winds, — wail,

All a - long, a - long, a - long The Col - or - a - do Trail.

THE TRAIL TO MEXICO

I made up my mind ___ in the ear - ly morn ___

To leave the home ___ where I was born ___

And leave my dar - - - - - ling _ girl be - hind, ___

For she said her heart ___ was _ on - ly mine. ___

Oh, when I held her in my arms,
I thought she had ten thousand charms.
Her kisses were so very sweet;
She said, "We'll be married when next we meet."

It was in the year of eighty-three
That A. J. Stinson hired me;
He said, "Young fellow, I want you to go
And follow my herd down to Mexico."

It was in the springtime of the year
That I took the trail and drove those steers,
And it was a long and a lonesome go
To drive those steers into Mexico.

When I got there in Mexico
I thought of that girl who loved me so;
I wrote a letter then to my dear,
But not one word from her did I hear.

So I started back to my own loved home;
I asked for that gal whom I adored.
She said, "Young man, I've wed a richer life;
Therefore, wild cowboy, seek another wife."

Oh, curse your gold and your silver, too,
And curse the girl who can't prove true;
I'm going back where the bullets fly
And stay on the trail till the day I die.

THE COWBOY'S HEAVEN

Last night as I lay on the prai - rie _____ And looked at the

stars in the sky, _____ I won - dered if ev - er a cow - boy _____

_ Would drift to that sweet by - and - by. _____ Roll on,

roll on, Roll on, lit - tle do - gies, roll on, roll on; Roll

on, roll on, Roll on, lit - tle do - gies, roll on. _____

THE COWBOY'S HEAVEN

Unlike the cowboys who were rowdy and untamed, there were many who were religious and took life seriously. Then, too, some of the wild cowboys sometimes worried whether the kind of life they were living was a good one. This song puts the cowboy's religion in terms of a great roundup, so that he can understand it and remember it easily. It tells him that if he behaves himself he will get to heaven; but if he doesn't, he'll be cut in with the rusties—the cattle that aren't good for anything but to be shot for their hides.

You may recognize the tune to this song; it is much like that of *My Bonnie Lies Over the Ocean*.

The road to that bright, happy region
Is a dim, narrow trail, so they say;
But the one that leads to perdition
Is posted and blazed all the way.
(*Chorus*)
They say there will be a great roundup,
And cowboys like dogies will stand
To be marked by the Riders of Judgment,
Who are posted and know every brand.
(*Chorus*)
I wonder if ever a cowboy
Stood ready for that Judgment Day
And could say to the Boss of the Riders,
"I'm ready; come drive me away."
(*Chorus*)
I know there are many stray cowboys
Who'll be lost at that great final sale,
When they might have gone on to green pastures
If they'd known of that dim, narrow trail.
(*Chorus*)

For they, like the steers that are locoed,
Stampede at the sight of a hand;
They're dragged with a rope to the roundup
Or get marked with some crooked man's brand.
(*Chorus*)
And I'm scared that I'll be a stray yearling,
A maverick, unbranded on high,
And get cut in the bunch with the rusties
When the Boss of the Riders goes by.
(*Chorus*)
For they tell of another big owner
Who's ne'er overstocked, so they say,
But who'll always make room for the sinner
Who drifts from the straight, narrow way.
(*Chorus*)
They say he will never forget you,
That he knows every action and look,
So for safety you'd better get branded;
Get your name in the great Tally Book.
(*Chorus*)

GOODBYE, OLD PAINT

The cowboy who sings *Goodbye, Old Paint* is leaving Cheyenne, Wyoming, to go to Montana, leaving his best friend, a paint horse, behind him. The horse has grown old and can no longer keep up with the younger horses, although he still tries to do the best he can.

The cowboy is also saying farewell to his sweetheart, Polly. She asks him to stay and sit with her while his horses eat some hay. But the cowboy tells her that his horses aren't hungry, the chuck wagon has already left and is rumbling down the trail, and he must go with his outfit. The last note of tender affection is reserved for old Paint; the cowboy is sorrier to leave his horse than his sweetheart.

Sometimes this song is sung to the tune of the first two lines of *The Railroad Corral*, and the chorus of "Goodbye, old Paint, I'm leaving Cheyenne" is sung after each verse to the same tune those words have in the first stanza of this version.

One form of entertainment the cowboy enjoyed was the square dance, when he could get to one. Often *Goodbye, Old Paint* was sung after the last dance, as the cowboys prepared to leave town and ride back to the ranch or the trail camp. For that reason, it's a good song to end this book.

69

GOODBYE, OLD PAINT

I'm leav - ing Chey - enne, I'm off for Mon - tan'; Good -
bye, old Paint, I'm leav - ing Chey - enne.

Old Paint's a good pony, he paces when he can;
Goodbye, old Paint, I'm leaving Cheyenne.

"Go unhitch your horses and give them some hay
And sit here beside me as long as you stay."

My horses aren't hungry, they won't eat your hay;
My wagon is loaded and rolling away.

My foot's in the stirrup, my bridle's in my hand;
So fare thee well, Polly, my horses won't stand.

Goodbye, old Paint, I'm leaving Cheyenne;
Goodbye, old Paint, I'm off for Montan'.